BENJAMIN BRITTEN

THE YOUNG PERSON'S GUIDE TO THE ORCHESTRA

OPUS 34

VARIATIONS AND FUGUE
ON A THEME OF PURCELL

BOOSEY & HAWKES

Boosey & Hawkes Music Publishers Ltd
www.boosey.com

The "Young Person's Guide to the Orchestra" should be performed with the inserted commentary, spoken by the conductor. The music is arranged so that the orchestra can continue playing at those moments when the conductor is speaking. A separate speaker can be used for the commentary if preferred.

In order to facilitate performance, a slightly different version omitting the spoken commentary is included in the score. The version without commentary, cuts or alters, in some instances, some bars between the sections of the theme and between the single variations. These instances are indicated as follows :

Bars to be played only in the version with the commentary are bracketed thus 1 : bars marked 2 apply to the version without the commentary only.

Notes printed in small type apply only to the version without commentary.

There are sometimes cuts marked with "vi-de" which, of course, refer only to the version without commentary.

Sometimes there are single bars "repeated ad libitum" so as to allow the speaker sufficient time. These bars are only to be played twice in the version without commentary. In addition the conductor will forego many pauses which are bracketed and linger less during the transitions if the commentary is not spoken.

This work is affectionately inscribed
to the children of
John and Jean Maud
Humphrey, Pamela, Caroline and Virginia,
for their edification and entertainment

Benjamin Britten, Op. 34

The Young Person's Guide to the Orchestra

Variations and Fugue
on a Theme of Purcell

The commentary written by Eric Crozier

To be spoken before the music starts:

The composer has written this piece of music specially to introduce you to the instruments of the orchestra. There are four teams of players; the STRINGS, the WOODWIND, the BRASS, and the PERCUSSION. Each of these four teams uses instruments which have a family likeness. They make roughly the same kind of sound in the same way. The STRINGS are played with a bow or plucked by the fingers. The WOODWIND are blown by the breath. The BRASS are blown too. The PERCUSSION are banged. First you will hear a Theme by the great English composer, Henry Purcell, played by the whole orchestra and by each one of the four groups of instruments.

Instrumentation

Piccolo
2 Flutes
2 Oboes
2 Clarinets in B♭ and A
2 Bassoons
4 Horns in F
2 Trumpets in C
3 Trombones
Tuba
Timpani
*Percussion (3+)
Harp
Strings

*bass drum/cymbals/tambourine; triangle/side drum/Chinese block/xylophone; castanets/gong/whip.

Duration with spoken commentary: c. 19 minutes
Duration without commentary: c. 17 minutes

The music to **The Young Person's Guide to the Orchestra** was originally written for the film 'The Instruments of the Orchestra'.

Allegro maestoso e largamente
THEME A
Piccolo
Flutes I & II
Oboes I & II
Clarinets in B♭ I & II
Bassoons I & II
I & II Horns in F III & IV
Trumpets in C I & II
I & II Trombones III (Bass) & Tuba
Timpani
Percussion
S.D.
B.D.
Xylo.
Cym.
Harp
sonoro
a2
marc.
Allegro maestoso e largamente
Violin I
Violin II
Viola
Cello
Bass
div.

*) Cut to [2] if commentary is not spoken

*) Bars marked 2 if commentary is not spoken.

THEME B
Picc.
f sost.
Flts. I & II
f sost.
Oboes I & II
f sost.
Clts. in B♭ I & II
f sost.
Bsns. I & II
f sost.
I & II
Hns. in F
III & IV
Trpts. in C I & II
I & II
Trombs.
III & Tuba
pp
Timp.
pp
Cym.
pp
Harp
pp
Vln. I
pp
Vln. II
pp
Vla.
pp
'Cello
pp
Bass
pp

Picc.
Flts. I & II
Oboes I & II
Clts. in B♭ I & II
Bsns. I & II
I & II Hns. in F III & IV
Trpts. in C I & II
I & II Trombs. III & Tuba
Timp.
Perc.
Harp
The first BRASS instruments were trumpets and hunting-horns.
These are their modern descendants.
Vln. I
Vln. II
Vla.
'Cello
Bass
pp
ppp

THEME C
Picc.
Flts. I & II
Oboes I & II
Clts. in B♭ I & II
Bsns. I & II
I & II
Hns. in F
III & IV
a 2
Trpts. in C I & II
I & II
Trombs.
III & Tuba
Timp.
Perc.
Harp
Vln. I
Vln. II
Vla.
'Cello
Bass

*)
1
*)
2
Picc.
Flts. I & II
Oboes I & II
Clts. in B♭ I & II
Bsns. I & II
I & II
Hns. in F
III & IV
Trpts. in C I & II
I & II
Trombs.
III & Tuba
Timp.
Perc.
Harp
The STRINGS, large and small, are scraped with a bow
or plucked with the fingers.
Their cousin the Harp is always plucked.
Vln. I
Vln. II
Vla.
'Cello
Bass
ff
pp

*) As before

THEME D

Picc.
Flts. I & II
Oboes I & II
Clts. in B♭ I & II
Bsns. I & II
Hns. in F I & II
III & IV
Trpts. in C I & II
Trombs. I & II
III & Tuba
Timp.
Perc.
Harp
Vln. I
Vln. II
Vla.
'Cello
Bass
marc.
pizz.
arco
f
ff

*) Cut if commentary is not spoken

THEME E
Picc.
Flts. I & II
Oboes I & II
Clts. in B♭ I & II
Bsns. I & II
I & II Hns. in F III & IV
Trpts. in C I & II
I & II Trombs. III & Tuba
Timp.
Tria.
Tamb.
S.D.
Cym.
B.D.
Harp
Vln. I
Vln. II
Vla.
'Cello
Bass
f marc.
poco a poco cresc.

THEME F
Picc.
Flts. I & II
a2
Oboes I & II
Clts. in B♭ I & II
Bsns. I & II
I & II
Hns. in F
III & IV
Trpts. in C I & II
(fp)
(f)
I & II
Trombs.
III & Tuba
Timp.
Xyl.
S.D.
Cym.
B.D.
marc.
ff
fp
ffz
sonoro
Harp
Vln. I
Vln. II
Vla.
'Cello
Bass
div.

Picc.
Flts. I & II
Oboes I & II
Clts. in B♭ I & II
Bsns. I & II
I & II
Hns. in F
III & IV
Trpts. in C I & II
I & II
Trombs.
III & Tuba
Timp.
Xyl.
S.D.
Cym.
B.D.
Harp
Vln. I
Vln. II
Vla.
'Cello
Bass
a 2
marc.
(fp)
fp
sf
f
tr

Now let us hear each instrument play a variation of its own. The highest of the Woodwind team is the clear, sweet voice of the FLUTE, with its shrill little brother, the PICCOLO.

*) Small notes of Flutes and Harp to be played if commentary is not spoken.

VARIATION A
Picc.
I
Flts.
II
Tria.
Harp
Vln. I
Vln. II
Harp *)
*) as before
p cresc.
pp
cresc.
trem.
poco cresc.
div.
ff
p
mf
mf pp
etc.

*) as before

Picc.
I
Flts.
II
Tria.
Harp
Vln. I
Vln. II
G major
(E)

OBOES have a gentle, plaintive quality, but they can be forceful enough when the composer wants them to.

Oboes I & II
Timp.
Vla.
'Cello div.
Bass
larg.
ff
rall.
p dim.
pp
cresc.
f
ppp
(pizz.)
CLARINETS are very agile. They make a beautifully smooth, mellow sound.
VARIATION C
Moderato
Clts. in B♭ I
II
Tuba
Vln. I
Vln. II
Vla.
'Cello
f sempre
pizz.
pizz. (non div.)
unis. pizz.
unis. pizz.

rall.
a tempo
I
Clts. in B♭
II
f espress.
p
f
p
Tuba
pp
rall.
a tempo
Vln. I
mf
Vln. II
p
Vla.
p
'Cello
p
cresc.
cresc.
cresc.
cresc.
cresc.
cresc.
cresc.

I
Clts. in B♭
II
Tuba
Vln. I
Vln. II
Vla.
'Cello
ff
20
(rubato)
mf
f
pp
p
dim.
pp dim.
pp morendo
ppp
BASSOONS are the largest of the Wood-wind team, so they have the deepest voices.

VARIATION D

Allegro alla marcia

*) Play 1 if commentary is spoken, 2 if it is not spoken.

VARIATION E

Brillante – alla polacca

Bsns. I & II
a 2
I & II
Hns. in F
III & IV
Trpt. II in C
I & II
Trombs.
III & Tuba
B.D.
Vln. I
Vln. II
cresc.
espress.
(sul G)

*) Repeat this bar only once if commentary is not spoken.

VARIATION F

Flts. I & II
Oboes I & II
Clts. in B♭ I & II
Bsns. I & II
I & II
Hns. in F
III & IV
I & II
Trombs.
III & Tuba
Via.
poco
espress.
(rall.)
Timp.
CELLOS sing with splendid richness and warmth. Listen to this fine sound!
2 Sole
cresc.
dim.
Via. div.

VARIATION G

a 2
Clts. in B♭ I & II
pp
Hn. IV in F
pp
Harp
poco p
I Sola
simile
Vla.
pp sempre
II Sola
simile
pp sempre
'Cello
pp lusingando
Clts. in B♭ I & II
Hn. IV in F
Harp
Vla.
'Cello
espress.
pp

Clts. in B♭ I & II
a 2
cresc.
f dim.
Hn. IV in F
pp
mf
dim.
Harp
cresc.
ff dim.
I Sola
II Sola
Vla.
cresc.
f dim.
'Cello
più
f molto espress. e dim.
Bsn. I
p sempre più
rall.
ppp
sempre più p
The DOUBLEBASSES are the grandfathers of the String family, with heavy, grumbling voices.
p sempre più
sempre più p
ppp

VARIATION H

Comminciando lento ma poco a poco accel.
Picc.
Flts. I & II
Oboes I & II
Bsns. I & II
Tamb.
Bass
pp
ppp
cresc.
(p) (cresc.)
pp
poco a poco cresc.
al
Allegro
ff
ffz
f
fz
veloce
gliss.
sf
a 2
pp stacc.
mf espress.

Flts. I & II
Oboes I & II
Bsns. I & II
Bass
Tamb.
Picc.
a 2
cresc.
ff
rall. molto
f
commínciando lento
ma accel.
pp
poco a poco cresc.
al
Allegro
ffz
pp stacc.
fz
veloce
gliss.

*) Cut this bar if commentary is not spoken.

VARIATION I

Maestoso (♩ = ♩)

I & II
Hns. in F
III & IV
Trpts. in C
I & II
I & II
Trombs.
III & Tuba
con sord.
senza sord.
Cym.
Gong
poco cresc.
dim.
Harp
sf
sf cresc.
fff con bravura
Vln. I
Vln. II
Vla.
'Cello
Bass
mf
dim.
pp
ppp
div.
1 *)
2 *)
The Brass family begins with the HORNS. These are made from brass tubing coiled into a circle.

*) as before

VARIATION J
L'istesso tempo
I & II
Hns. in F
III & IV
Timp.
Harp
Vla.
'Cello
Bass
mf cresc.
mf cresc.
più f
ff
ffz dim.
p dolciss.
f cresc.
S.D. sticks
ppp
mf
pp
nat.
2 Sole
pp espress.
2 Soli
ppp trem. pont.
cresc.
arco
pizz.
cresc. molto
cresc.
pp sempre

I & II
Hns. in F
III & IV
Timp.
Harp
Vla.
'Cello
Bass
Tutte div. a 2
Tutti div. a 2
arco
trem. pont.
poco
dolcis.
rall.
(laissez vibrer)
I expect you all know the sound of TRUMPETS.
2 Sole
2 Soli
espress.
più p
pizz.

VARIATION K

Vivace
Trpts. in C I
Trpts. in C II
S.D.
Vln. I
Vln. II
Vla.
'Cello
stacc. sempre
pp cresc.
pp molto marcato
poco a poco cresc.
sempre stacc.
mf
f
dim.
ppp cresc.
pp cresc.
ppp

The TROMBONES have heavy brassy voices. The BASS TUBA is heavier still.

*) as before

VARIATION L

Allegro pomposo

Picc.
Flts. I & II
a 2
mf
Oboes I & II
mf
Clts. in A I & II
a 2
mf
Bsns. I & II
mf
I & III
Hns. in F
p
II & IV
p
Trpts. in C I & II
I & II
p
p
Trombs.
III
p
Tuba
f
p
Bass
p

Picc.
f
ff
Flts.
I & II
a 2
cresc molto
f
ff
Oboes
I & II
cresc molto
f
ff
Clts. in A
I & II
a 2
cresc molto
f
ff
Bsns.
I & II
a 2
cresc molto
f
ff
I & III
Hns. in F
II & IV
cresc molto
mf
f
Trpts. in C
I & II
p
mf
I & II
Trombs.
III
espress.
p
a 2
f
Tuba
espress.
p
f
Bass
cresc molto
mf
f

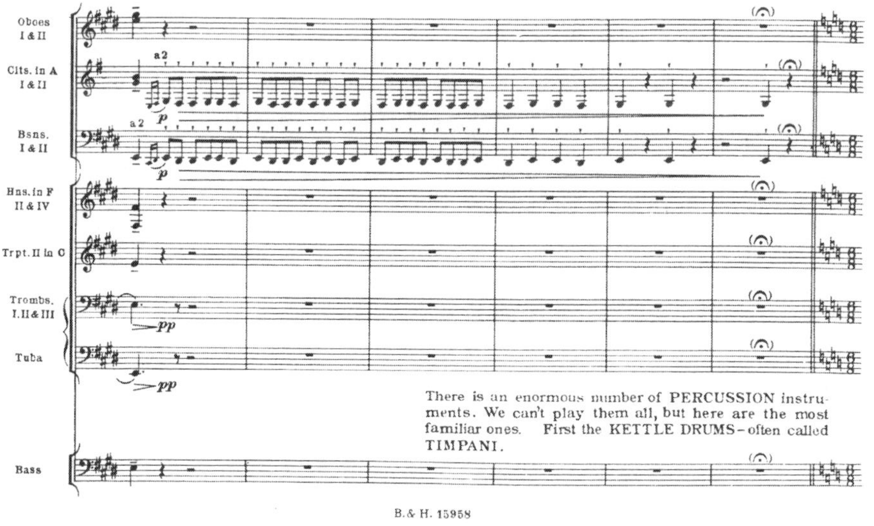

There is an enormous number of PERCUSSION instruments. We can't play them all, but here are the most familiar ones. First the KETTLE DRUMS – often called TIMPANI.

VARIATION M
Moderato
Timp.
Perc.
Vln. I
Vln. II
Vla.
'Cello
Bass
(Felt sticks)
mf distinto
p saltando
p saltando
p saltando
pizz.
p
pizz.
p
Timp.
ppp
Cym.
B. D.
mf
mf
The BASS DRUM
and CYMBALS
Vln. I
Vln. II
Vla.
'Cello
Bass
ppp
ppp
ppp
ppp
ppp
pizz.
p
pizz.
p
arco
p
arco
p

Timp.
Cym.
Tamb.
B.D.
The TAMBOURINE
and TRIANGLE
Vln. I
Vln. II
Vla.
'Cello
Bass
arco
pizz.
Tria.
The SIDE
DRUM and
(pizz.)

Timp.
S. D.
Ch. Block
Chinese Block
CHINESE BLOCK
Vln. I
Vln. II
Vla.
'Cello
Bass
arco
pizz.
Timp.
Xyl.
Perc.
The XYLOPHONE
Vln. I
Vln. II
Vla.
Cello
Bass
pizz.

Timp.
Cast.
The CASTANETS
and GONG
Vln. I
Vln. II
Vla.
'Cello
Bass
arco
col legno
ppp
f
Timp.
Gong
Whip
and before they all play together,
the WHIP.
Vln. I
Vln. II
Vla.
'Cello
Bass
arco
pizz.
sul pont.
pp
mf

* If there are not enough players for the percussion instruments, the Triangle and the Gong may be omitted for the next six bars *only.*

We have taken the whole Orchestra to pieces. Now let us put it together in a Fugue. The instruments come in one after another, in the same order as before— beginning with the Piccolo. At the end, the Brass will play Henry Purcell's fine melody, while

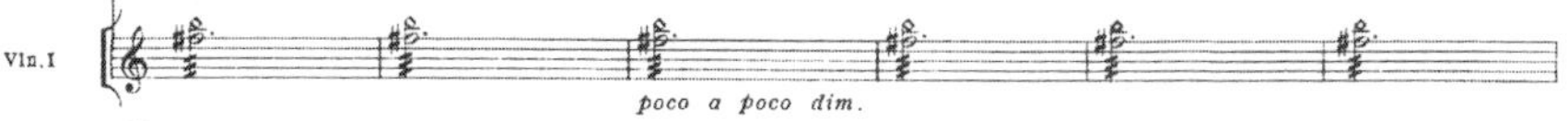

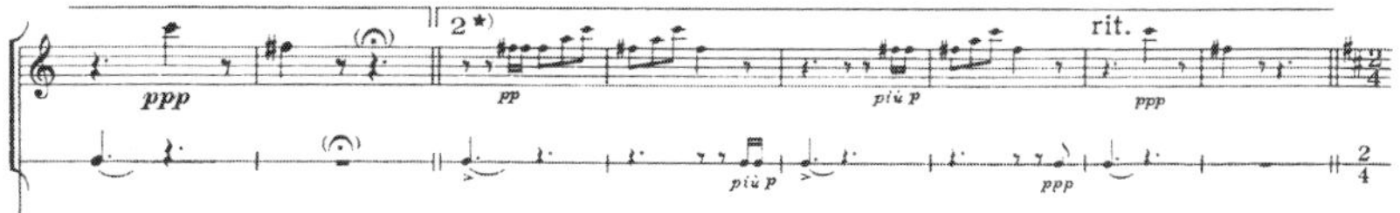

the others go on playing Benjamin Britten's Fugue.

*) as before

FUGUE
Allegro molto
Picc.
A
Flts. I & II
a 2
B
Oboes I & II
C
Clts. in B♭ I & II
p
pp
mp
mf
(pp)
cresc.

D
Picc.
Flts. I & II
Oboes I & II
Clts. in B♭ I & II
Bsns. I & II
a 2
f
pp
p
ff
cresc.
E
Vln. I
sf

Picc.
Flts. I & II
Oboes I & II
Clts. in B♭ I & II
I
Bsns.
II
Vln. I
Vln. II
p
F
Picc.
Flts. I & II
Oboes I & II
Clts. in B♭ I & II
Bsns. I & II
Vln. I
Vln. II
Vla.
F
p
f

G
Picc.
Flts. I & II
Oboes I & II
Clts. in B♭ I & II
Bsns. I & II
a 2
cresc.
Vln. I
Vln. II
Vla.
'Cello
H
Bass
ff con tutta forza

Picc.
I
Flts.
II
I
Oboes
II
I
Clts. in B♭
II
I
Bsns.
II
Vln. I
Vln. II
Vla.
'Cello
Bass
cresc.
mf
f

I
Picc.
I
Flts.
II
I
Oboes
II
I
Clts. in B♭
II
I
Bsns.
II
pp
pp
Solo
Harp
f
I
Vln. I
Vln. II
Vla.
'Cello
Bass
ff
dim.
pp
pizz.

Picc.
I
Flts.
II
pp
I
Oboes
II
pp
pp
I
Clts. in B♭
II
pp
pp
I
Bsns.
II
pp
pp
Harp
f sempre
Vln. I
pp
Vln. II
pp
arco
pp
Vla.
pp
arco
pp
'Cello
pp
arco
pp
Bass
arco
pp

J
Picc.
I
Flts.
II
I
Oboes
II
I
Clts. in B♭
II
I
Bsns.
II
I
II
Hns. in F
III
IV
Harp
F major
f sempre
J
arco
Vln. I
Vln. II
Vla.
'Cello
Bass
pp
cresc.
ff
p
f

K
Picc.
I
Flts.
II
I
Oboes
II
I
Clts. in B♭
II
a 2
Bsns.
I & II
I
II
Hns. in F
III
IV
I
Trpts. in C
II
Harp
B♭ major
F major
G♭ major
Vln. I
Vln. II
Vla.
'Cello
Bass

Picc.
Flts. I & II
Oboes I & II
Clts. in B♭ I & II
Bsns. I & II
Hns. in F I & II
III & IV
Trpts. in C I
II
Harp
D♭ major
Vln. I
Vln. II
Vla.
'Cello
Bass
a 2
mf
ff
cresc.

⊕ Quasi glissando

* Tambourine ad lib.

Picc.
Flts. I & II
Oboes I & II
Clts. in B♭ I & II
Bsns. I & II
Hns. in F I & II
III & IV
a 2
Trpts. in C I & II
Trombs. I, II & III
a 3
Tuba
Timp.
Xyl.
Cym.
B.D.
Tamb.
S.D.
Harp
Vln. I
Vln. II
Vla.
'Cello
Bass
cresc. molto
cresc.
p
f

Con slancio (l'istesso tempo)
Picc.
Flts. I & II
Oboes I & II
Clts. in B♭ I & II
Bsns. I & II
I & II
Hns. in F
III & IV
Trpts. in C I & II
I & II
Trombs.
III & Tuba
Timp.
Xyl.
Cym.
Gong
Tamb.
S.D.
Harp
Vln. I
Vln. II
Vla.
'Cello
Bass
a 2
dim.
pp
ff
f
sost.
sf
mf
marcatiss.
unis.

Picc.
Flts.
I & II
a 2
Oboes
I & II
a 2
Clts. in B♭
I & II
a 2
Bsns.
I & II
a 2
I & II
Hns. in F
III & IV
a 2
Trpts. in C
I & II
f
I & II
Trombs.
III & Tuba
B.D.
mf
Harp
Vln. I
Vln. II
Vla.
'Cello
Bass

Picc.
Flts. I & II
a 2
Oboes I & II
Clts. in B♭ I & II
Bsns. I & II
I & II
Hns. in F
III & IV
Trpts. in C I & II
I & II
Trombs.
III & Tuba
Cym.
B. D.
Harp
Vln. I
Vln. II
Vla.
'Cello
Bass
più f
mf

Picc.
Flts. I & II
a 2
Oboes I & II
a 2
Clts. in B♭ I & II
a 2
Bsns. I & II
a 2
ff sempre sost.
I & II Hns. in F III & IV
ff sempre sost.
ff sempre sost.
Trpts. in C I & II
ff
I & II Trombs. III & Tuba
ff sempre sost.
ff sempre sost.
Cym.
più f
Gong
p
B.D.
Harp
8
Vln. I
Vln. II
Vla.
'Cello
ff sempre sost.
Bass
ff sempre sost.

Picc.
Flts. I & II
a 2
Oboes I & II
Clts. in B♭ I & II
Bsns. I & II
Hns. in F I & II
III & IV
Trpts. in C I & II
Trombs. I & II
III & Tuba
Gong
poco a poco cresc.
Harp
ff
Vln. I
Vln. II
Vla.
'Cello
Bass

Animato
Picc.
a 2
Flts. I & II
Oboes I & II
Clts. in B♭ I & II
Bsns. I & II
I & II
Hns. in F
III & IV
Trpts. in C I & II
I & II
Trombs.
III & Tuba
Hard sticks
Timp.
S.D.
Cym.
Gong
B.D.
Harp
Animato
Vln. I
Vln. II
Vla.
'Cello
Bass

Printed by Halstan:
Halstan UK, 2–10 Plantation Road, Amersham, Bucks, HP6 6HJ. United Kingdom
Halstan DE, Weißliliengasse 4, 55116 Mainz. Germany

Benjamin Britten: Selected Works

Operas and Ballets

A Midsummer Night's Dream op 64
Albert Herring op 39
The Beggar's Opera op 43 realisation
Billy Budd op 50
Gloriana op 53
Let's Make an Opera (The Little Sweep) op 45
Noye's Fludde op 59
Peter Grimes op 33
The Prince of the Pagodas op 57
The Rape of Lucretia op 37
The Turn of the Screw op 54

Symphonic Works

Canadian Carnival op 19
The Courtly Dances from 'Gloriana'
Diversions op 21
Four Sea Interludes from 'Peter Grimes' op 33a
Matinées musicales op 24
Mont Juic op 12
Pas de six from 'The Prince of the Pagodas' op 57a
Passacaglia from 'Peter Grimes' op 33b
Piano Concerto op 13
Prelude and Dances from 'The Prince of the Pagodas' op 57b
Prelude and Fugue op 29
Scottish Ballad op 26
Sinfonia da Requiem op 20
Sinfonietta op 1
Soirées musicales op 9
Symphonic Suite from 'Gloriana' op 53a
Symphony for Cello and Orchestra op 68
Variations on a Theme of Frank Bridge op 10
Violin Concerto op 15
The Young Person's Guide to the Orchestra op 34

Instrumental Music

Alpine Suite *recorder trio*
Fanfare for St Edmundsbury *3 trumpets*
Holiday Diary op 5 *piano*
Introduction and Rondo alla Burlesca op 23 no 1 *2 pianos*
Lachrymae op 48 *viola & piano*
Mazurka Elegiaca op 23 no 2 *2 pianos*
Night Piece (Notturno) *piano*
Phantasy op 2 *oboe, violin, viola & cello*
Prelude and Fugue on a Theme of Vittoria *organ*
Scherzo *recorder quartet*
Six Metamorphoses after Ovid op 49 *oboe*
Sonata in C op 65 *cello & piano*
String Quartet no 1 in D op 25
String Quartet no 2 in C op 36
Suite op 6 *violin & piano*

Songs and Song-Cycles

The Birds
Canticle I 'My Beloved is Mine' op 40
Canticle II 'Abraham and Isaac' op 51
Canticle III 'Still Falls the Rain' op 55
A Charm of Lullabies op 41
Evening, Morning, Night
Fish in the Unruffled Lakes Six Settings of W H Auden
Folksong Arrangements
The Holy Sonnets of John Donne op 35
Les Illuminations op 18
Nocturne op 60
Now Sleeps the Crimson Petal
On this Island op 11
Our Hunting Fathers op 8
Sechs Hölderlin-Fragmente op 61
Serenade op 31
Seven Sonnets of Michelangelo op 22
Songs from the Chinese op 58
Three Songs from 'The Heart of the Matter'
Two Ballads
Winter Words op 52

Choral Works

Advance Democracy
Antiphon op 56b
Ballad of Heroes op 14
The Ballad of Little Musgrave and Lady Barnard
Cantata Academica, Carmen Basiliense op 62
Cantata Misericordium op 69
A Ceremony of Carols op 28
Choral Dances from 'Gloriana'
Festival Te Deum op 32
Five Flower Songs op 47
Friday Afternoons op 7
A Hymn of St Columba
Hymn to St Cecilia op 27
Hymn to St Peter op 56a
A Hymn to the Virgin
Missa Brevis in D op 63
Psalm 150 op 67
Rejoice in the Lamb op 30
Saint Nicolas op 42
Song: We are the Darkness in the Heat of the Day
Spring Symphony op 44
War Requiem op 66
A Wedding Anthem op 46

BOOSEY & HAWKES

AN IMAGEM COMPANY

Ad 272

SELECTED CONTEMPORARY SCORES

A complete list of our extensive library of contemporary scores is available on request. For more information about Boosey & Hawkes composers visit our website.

John ADAMS
Chamber Symphony
Short Ride in a Fast Machine
The Wound-Dresser

Louis ANDRIESSEN
De Staat
De Stijl
De Tijd

Harrison BIRTWISTLE
Pulse Shadows
The Shadow of Night
Theseus Game

Elliott CARTER
In Sleep, in Thunder
String Quartets nos 4 & 5
Triple Duo

Unsuk CHIN
Gougalōn
Violin Concerto

Henryk Mikołaj GÓRECKI
Kleines Requiem für eine Polka
Old Polish Music

HK GRUBER
Aerial
Cello Concerto

Magnus LINDBERG
Cantigas
Clarinet Concerto
Violin Concerto

James MACMILLAN
Piano Concertos nos 2 & 3
Tryst
Veni, Veni, Emmanuel

Peter MAXWELL DAVIES
Eight Songs for a Mad King
An Orkney Wedding, with Sunrise
Symphonies nos 1–8

Einojuhani RAUTAVAARA
Manhattan Trilogy

Steve REICH
Different Trains
Music for 18 Musicians
Tehillim

Christopher ROUSE
Flute Concerto
Symphony no 2

Mark-Anthony TURNAGE
Chicago Remains
Frieze
From the Wreckage

Ad 497

BOOSEY & HAWKES

AN IMAGEM COMPANY